The 2024 Railway Quiz Book

from The Transport Treasury

The
· Transport ·
Treasury

www.ttpublishing.co.uk

ISBN 978-1-915281-06-7

First published in 2023 by Transport Treasury Publishing Limited.
16 Highworth Close, High Wycombe HP13 7PJ

www.ttpublishing.co.uk

Printed by Short Run Press, Exeter.

Publishers note:

Would you like to be part of the next edition of the QUIZ book?

Transport Treasury Publishing welcome contributions of questions
(and answers!) in time for the next edition of the quiz book.

All subjects and topics are welcome including those not covered
in this edition.

Illustrated questions are also welcome and you must have permission
for the photograph to be used.

Contents

Introduction   4

1   GWR/WR   7

2   SR and Constituents   13

3   LMS/LMR   19

4   LNER/ER   23

5   Scottish Railways   27

6   BR Standard Steam   29

7   Modern Traction 1   33

8   Signalling and Trackwork   37

9   Accidents   41

10   Railway Reading   45

11   Personalities   49

12   Modern Traction 2   53

13   Railway Geography   57

14   UK Railways since Privatisation   61

15   Pot Pourri   65

Answers   68

Welcome to the 2024 Transport Treasury Railway Quiz Book

At Transport Treasury, railways are our passion and it is a passion we are now delighted to share with you in the pages that follow.

Most of you will be aware of the expanding range of book titles we publish, as well as the similarly expanding archive of images we make available to enthusiasts and others.

In consequence to both of these it has been a privilege to get to know a growing range of authors, all experts in their own field, several of whom have agreed to pick their own brains for the amusement of their colleagues and now we are sure a wider audience.

In what follows is a range of carefully thought-out questions, some written, some pictorial but all intended to test as well as tease your own knowledge.

There is no such thing as a railway 'expert', the subject is far too vast encompassing as it does, history, different companies, geography, personalities, steam, diesel, electric, rolling stock, stations, engineering, etc.

In addition the term 'I like railways' or 'he/she likes railways' could mean any of the above or an interest in collecting; photographs, models, artefacts, or volunteering on a heritage railway. This is why we say there is no such thing as a railway 'expert'.

Accordingly in what follows we have tried to include something for just about everyone. From the historic to the modern, from rolling stock to operation, and from geography even to railway publishing – after all if you are reading this you will almost certainly have a selection of books nearby.

Some questions are also deliberately easy, others intentionally not so, but having tried out the formula on some of our own friends and contacts the responses were positive and we are now proud to make many of these questions available to a wider audience.

In addition there are some which may almost appear to ask the same question twice; be assured it is deliberate, just a gentle tease to see you are on your toes.

So off we go – and to get you in the mood, try this one for size;

What two types of BR Standard steam designs had oval buffers, and why...?

(You could look at the image on the last page for one of the answers!)

It should be straightforward but if you are in doubt, you will find the answer, along with all the other answers starting on page 68. You could of course cheat – but we trust you!

Good luck from all the team at The Transport Treasury!

Nice and easy to start; what is this vehicle? (See page 69 for the answer.)

Graham Smith courtesy Richard Sissons

Bonus question; The location is of course Sonning Cutting just east of Reading and the train has a 'Hymek' at the front (sorry it was not going to be that easy). So if the train is heading towards London which line is it on?

Paul Hocquard

Section 1
GWR/WR

As with all – well most of the questions – you could probably find the answer on the internet, but have a go without the technology first. Delving deep into the grey cells and/or a book can be so much more rewarding.

1. In what year was the original Great Western Railway incorporated?

2. And to make up for such an easy start, a locomotive question, what was the number and name (if it has a name that at least narrows it down a bit) of the locomotive fitted with Lentz style rotary cam poppett valves in 1931?

3. Still on the subject of locomotives but moving into the BR(W) era. In 1951 Swindon undertook controlled road testing on a locomotive class from another region. What class of engine – give yourself a bonus if you can find the number – and what was the purpose of these tests?

4. The GWR came into conflict, or should we say competition with its rivals at several locations. Plymouth, Exeter, Gloucester, etc. At Exeter for example passengers might leave for London in different directions; GWR towards Taunton and SR to Exeter Queen Street/Central. Where in Wiltshire might London passengers also have departed in different directions?

5. As a means of economy, the GWR introduced the Motor Economic System of Maintenance on several cross-country and branch lines from the late 1920s onwards. Which was the first?

6. When were red distant signals abolished on the GWR?

7. Associated with the above, the controlling signal lever was also now painted yellow – to correspond with the new colour for distant signals. But what had the controlling lever been painted when distant signals had a red arm?

8. At Reading and elsewhere and in the days of slip coach working, there existed what were known as 'slipping distants'. What were these and what was their purpose?

9. At the Westbury complex there were several junctions both on the avoiding line and within the station complex. What was the name of the wartime connection/junction which bypassed the immediate station area and allowed trains to come from the north; Bath or Thingley – and then turn east towards Reading?

10. What was the gauge of the Lee Moor Tramway that dissected the GWR at Laira and then ran parallel with the railway for some distance?

11. The short branch line from Chippenham to Calne provided a very useful, and indeed lucrative, traffic from the terminus. What was this traffic?

12. If the last one was a bit difficult, this one is sweeter. What traffic came out of Keynsham, near Bristol? (And if you are old enough to recall listening to Radio Luxembourg, you may well remember a certain Mr. Horace Bachelor extolling the virtues of his 'infra-draw' method of winning the pools. Listeners were invited to write in hence his address was broadcast and with the town spelt K-E-Y-N-S-H-A-M Keynshammmmm, Bristol.)

13. The GWR only ever had two route-setting signalling installations; 'route-setting' meaning the operation of one lever to set up a complete route. One was at Newport, but it was preceded for a short time by a smaller installation, where was this?

14. The GWR used telegraph codes to describe its different types of rolling stock, goods and passenger, 'Toad' for goods brake van being one of the better known. The rationale was that during the days of the telegraph sending a message like 'brake van required', took up far more time on the wires compared with 'Send Toad'. So how well do you know some of the designations? Try this one: 'Snake'?

15. The Northern Division of the GWR had its own locomotive superintendent between 1854 and 1892. These were the two Armstrong's, Joseph and George. Which one subsequently went on to be Locomotive Superintendent at Swindon?

16. At which GWR location was the famed 'snake notice' warning passengers of the likely presence of adders?

17. What is meant by the term 'inside keyed rail'?

A bonus and this time in three parts.

Firstly we have Hall No 6920 at Hatton.

Part A – what was the name of this engine?

Part B – what does the two lamp headcode mean?

Part C (really sneaky) – can you name the stations on the main Birmingham line either side of Hatton?

Image Henry Priestley

18. Most likely several readers have their own private collections of GWR ephemera and paperwork possibly including a GWR clock. There were several designs of the latter, various wooden case examples, some very ornate and also the ubiquitous brass drum clock once commonplace in signal boxes. Two parts to this question (but you need both to score the point); firstly where were the GWR clock workshops where clocks were sent for repair (in the 20th century), and secondly, who was the maker of most if not all of those brass drum clocks?

19. A question now to test your knowledge of GWR geography. What station on the former Cambrian lines was the junction for the Van railway?

20. And speaking of geography, there will not be anyone who will not have heard of Paddington and its associated steam depot at Old Oak Common. So another two-parter; firstly what was the name of the stabling point used by engines outside Paddington, and what depot did Old Oak Common replace?

21. The GWR acquired two 0-4-0 Sentinel shunters in the mid-1920s, numbered 12 and 13. One was used for a short time on a Wiltshire branch line; which line was this?

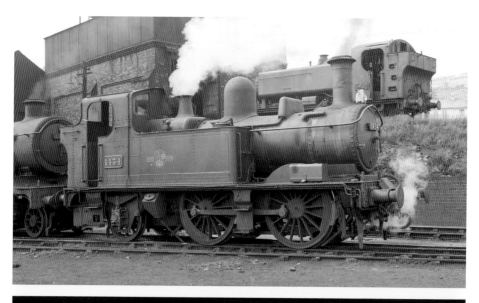

No 1434 at Laira shed on 15 July 1958. Introduced between 1932 and 1936, the 75 engines of this class were originally numbered in a different series, what was it and why?

R C Riley

22. Most will have heard of Sir Felix Pole, arguably perhaps the most revolutionary of the GWR general managers – perhaps even considered a bit too revolutionary for some which may explain his early departure from the company. So for one point – you have to get both to get the point – who were General Managers in office either side of Pole?

23. How many 'Super Saloons' were built by the GWR? (No bonus this time but can you name them?)

24. What was the name of the residence used by G. J. Churchward at Swindon, but subsequently demolished as the works expanded?

25. What was the vacuum (measured in inches of mercury) used by the GWR as compared with the other railway companies?

The 'twin shield' on the roof at Paddington. Having perhaps worked you hard over the last few pages, a nice easy one to finish with. Which locations do the shields represent?

SR and Constituents

1. In 1905 the London, Brighton & South Coast Railway embarked on an ambitious plan of overhead electrification which, had it remained an independent company, may well have seen expansion all the way to Brighton. What voltage was used?

2. Can you name the engineer who transferred from Swindon to Ashford and was involved with the development of the three cylinder Maunsell Mogul types?

3. What was the name of the terminus of the branch line west of Brighton where a Sentinel Railway was used for a time in the 1930s?

4. How many Bulleid pacific type locomotives were built after nationalisation – built NOT rebuilt?

5. The Southern Railway were adept at what we might nowadays call recycling; taking a locomotive type and rebuilding this into something more suitable. Can you name three steam classes where this took place under Southern Railway ownership?

6. What was the gauge of the original Torrington and Marland Railway replaced by the Southern Railway with a standard gauge line between Torrington and Halwill?

Opposite – a bonus question (and to make up for the GWR questions being far too easy). Here we have an interior view of one of Mr. Bulleid's 'Tavern Cars', introduced to what might well be described as a slightly bemused audience in May 1949. Paired with an almost windowless restaurant car they were criticised almost from day one although the novelty factor did much, it was said, towards increased takings. Two parts to this bonus, firstly they all carried 'pub' type identifications, how many can you name AND apart from on the Southern, what other region of British Railways did they work on?
British Railways

7. The Southern had locomotive works at Ashford, Brighton and Eastleigh. Where were the associated carriage works?

8. On its main lines the Southern made extensive use of a type of signalling system made by Sykes. What was it called?

9. The Southern was well known for its EMU descriptions; SUB meaning suburban and BEL meaning Brighton Belle (Pullman). So what did the designation HAL stand for?

10. The Ventnor West branch line had a life of just 52 years and having dubious distinction of being the first of the Island lines to close. Two parts to this question – and you have to get both right; what was the suffix given to the other Ventnor station – the one that lasted until 1966, and secondly what was the junction station for the Ventnor West branch where the line diverged?

11. Almost certainly all will have heard of Sir Eustace Missenden, General Manager of the Southern Railway during WW2, (he also had a locomotive named after him, No. 34090) but with which railway company did he start his railway career?

12. Why was there embarrassment and frustration for Mr. Bulleid and others when the first landing craft built at the Southern Railway works at Eastleigh in WW2 was lowered into Southampton water?

13. Who was the Southern Railway's official historian?

14. Under the Southern Railway where was the testing section of the Chief Mechanical Engineer based?

15. Exeter Central station will of course be well known, so another two-part question and again you need to get both. The first part is easy, what was the original name for Exeter Central station, and the more difficult one, when did it change names?

16. South of Guildford were two junctions; the first was the cross country line to Redhill and the second the branch to Christ's Hospital. What were the names of the two junctions? Both are needed.

17. What was the nickname of the original Southampton and Dorchester Railway, so called partly because of its promoter and partly because of the tortuous route taken via Ringwood and Wimborne?

18. Can you name either of two branch lines operated on alternate years by the LBSCR/LSWR and LSWR/GWR, one in Hampshire, the other Dorset? (The two routes are not connected other than by this unusual method of operating.)

A test of your railway geography now. Here we see M7 No. 30480 at Lymington Pier station. A ferry service operated from alongside the pier here – but to where? In addition we could be really nasty and ask what was the name of the short lived halt on this branch intended to serve the village of Sway before the opening of the first line from Brockenhurst to Christchurch in 1888?

Graham Smith courtesy Richard Sissons

19. A nice easy one now, what date was the formal start of the Bournemouth electrification and with it the elimination of steam on the Southern Region?

20. Boat trains were a regular feature of Southern Railway/Region passenger traffic and these had to be slotted into the timetable according to the sailing/arrival times of ocean-going ships, which was again dependent upon weather and tides. What were these variable paths in the timetables referred to where there was space for a boat train to be run?

21. Now one for the book worms. Four renowned and established authors were responsible for the seminal works on LSWR, LBSCR, SECR and Southern goods wagons (four volumes). You may well have them on your shelves, what are the author's surnames?

For those who have visited the Mid Hants Railway at Alresford, Ropley, Medstead & Four Marks, or Alton this should be a straightforward question.

Here we see an M7 loco No. 30356 exchanging the single line tablet with the signalman. The train is heading towards us and the locomotive is not propelling, so the question; what was the last station this train would have called at? (Branch passenger trains called at all stations on the line.)
Gerald Daniels

This is the terminus at Lyme Regis. In the background is one of three locomotives dating from the 19th century and still in daily use on the line in the early 60s. Who designed them and what was the class designation?
Gerald Daniels

22. The name Bulleid is of course well known, but where did he come from before his tenure on the Southern and where did he go to afterwards? Both answers need to be right.

23. The Western, the Midland, and the Eastern all had them on their locomotive tenders, the Southern did not – what was it the Southern did not have?

24. The Southern used to operate trains out of the Necropolis station at Waterloo – so where was the destination?

25. What two engines were sold by the LBSCR to the LSWR for the Lyme Regis branch, what were they and what were their numbers?

A nice straightforward one to start this section. Here we see Stanier designed 4-6-0 No. 44668 in workaday grime at Carlisle. What was the nickname given to this numerous class?

Graham Smith courtesy Richard Sissons

LMS/LMR

1. Arguably the greatest of the LMS Chief Mechanical Engineers was William Stanier. Before taking up his appointment with the LMS where did he come from?

2. What is the name of the junction north of Crewe where the line to Liverpool diverges?

3. The LMS sent their prestige 'Coronation Scot' train and locomotive No. 6220 named *Coronation* to America in 1939. However, the engine was not actually No. 6220 but another masquerading with the same number. What was the true identity of that engine?

4. What were the BR shed codes for Camden and Willesden?

5. The LMS had locomotive works at Crewe, Derby and Horwich but where was the principal coaching stock works?

6. How many principal stations once existed in the town of Blackpool?

7. Who were the designers of the original Euston?

8. Who was Lord Stamp?

9. Where did the accident occur involving *Fury* the experimental high-pressure locomotive?

10. Which senior official, who later went on to head mechanical engineering on British Railways, was on the footplate of No. 6201 *Princess Elizabeth* in 1933 on its debut test run to Glasgow and return in 1933?

11. What was the pre-nationalisation route mileage of the LMS?

12. How many Beyer-Garratt locomotives were operated by the LMS?

13. Who were the major constituent companies of the LMS, excluding joint lines?

14. Where was the location of the intended joint LMS/LNER locomotive testing plant but not actually opened by BR in 1948?

15. What was a 'Stove R'.

16. What was the name of the Princess class locomotive destroyed in the horrific 1952 accident at Harrow and Wealdstone?

17. Slightly off-piste now, the LMS had a station called 'Lichfield', but on what railway and where was there the similar sounding 'Litchfield' station?

18. How many members of the 'Black 5' class were fitted with outside Stephenson link valve gear?

19. What class of LMS tank engine was fitted with oval buffers?

20. A branch line to where, diverged at Beattock station?

21. What was a 'Baby Scot'?

22. Where were the LMS ferry ports in the north west for sailings to Ireland?

23. What is the height above sea level of Shap Summit?

24. How many arches are there on Ribblehead viaduct?

25. In what year was there a major accident at Ais Gill?

Opposite: What was the nickname of this engine which banked trains up the Lickey Incline at Bromsgrove? *JTC*

Top: What class of engine was *King George VI. R E Vincent*

Bottom: Where was this the entrance to the locomotive shed? *R E Vincent*

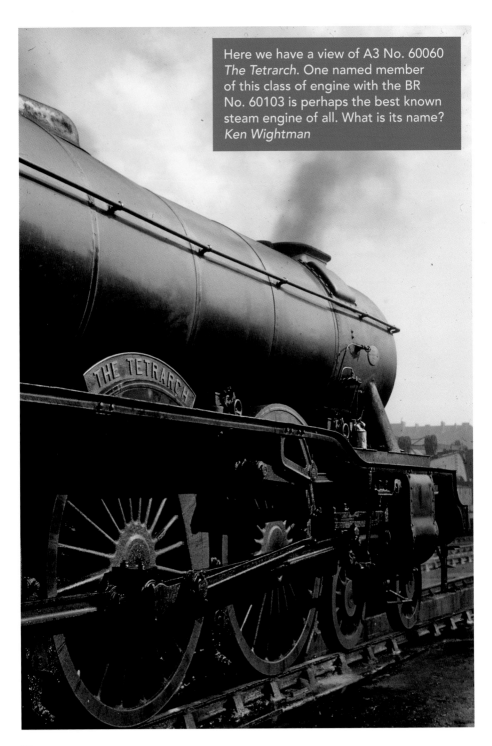

Here we have a view of A3 No. 60060 *The Tetrarch*. One named member of this class of engine with the BR No. 60103 is perhaps the best known steam engine of all. What is its name?
Ken Wightman

Section 4
LNER/ER

1. Where did the 'Elizabethan' train run between?

2. What was the nickname of LNER No. 10000?

3. Can you recall the name of BR's last shunting horse and used to shunt horse boxes at Newmarket?

4. What London terminus did the LNER inherit and from which trains to East Anglia departed?

5. The locomotive shed for Kings Cross was known by what nickname?

6. R. H. N. 'Dick' Hardy was famed for his reminiscences on the LNER and BR(E). Which London depot was he particularly involved with?

7. The Great Northern Railway, which operated the main line from Kings Cross had its main locomotive works in which town along the route?

8. Which route was known as the 'Last Main Line'.

9. During BR years the Eastern Region was split with a new North Eastern Region formed. Where did the NE Region have its headquarters?

10. What was a 'quad-art' set?

11. What was a Gresley P2?

12. When did the Forth Bridge open?

13. On what line was Takeley station?

14. What livery was used by the LNER for its regular passenger coaching stock (not excursion stock)?

15. The LNER adopted a letter classification for its steam locomotive types, 'A' was a 4-6-2, 'B' for a 4-6-0, 'C' for a 4-4-2 etc. What was 'J'?

16. The A4 is probably the most visually recognisable class of British steam locomotive. How many were built?

17. How many A4s are preserved (state all of their names)?

18. James Holden of the Great Eastern Railway built a solitary 0-10-0 tank engine in 1902 to ascertain if a steam engine might compete with the acceleration obtainable using electric power. What was its name and what became of it?

19. The LNER had three Chief Mechanical Engineers during its 25 year life. Can you name them?

20. In June 1944 an ammunition train exploded at Soham in Cambridgeshire causing much damage but far less than it might have had it not been for the heroic action of two railwayman. What gallantry medal did these two worthy individuals subsequently receive?

21. After 1948 but before the introduction of the 'Britannia' class, what type of engine class borrowed from elsewhere were tried out on the GE lines?

22. What was the 'Silver Jubilee'?

N2 0-6-2T No. 69504 engaged on shunting duty. What was the purpose of the curved pipe that ran from the smokebox back into the side tanks (one on either side)? *R C Riley*

This is A1 No. 60142 at speed. Unfortunately all the engines of this class were scrapped by British Railways but a 'new-build' has come into being in recent years and to rapturous applause wherever it goes. What is the name of the newest member of the class? *Ken Wightman*

23. What was a 'booster' as fitted to some LNER steam engines?

24. What type of electric locomotive was built in 1941 for the projected electrification of the Woodhead route?

25. Who was acting as General Manager of the LNER at the time of nationalisation in 1948?

Top: This is a view of B1 No. 61133 at Thornton Junction. So what in the 1960s was the first passenger station on the line that diverged to the left?

Bottom: This – now preserved – popular engine was closely linked with a BBC children's programme. What was it called?

Both images W. A. C. Smith

Section 5
Scottish Railways

1. 'Night Mail' was a 1936 British documentary film featuring the work of the Post Office between England and Scotland 'Over the Border'. The locomotive featured was a 4-6-0 'Royal Scot'. Who designed the 'Royal Scot' class?

2. The Highland railwaymen nicknamed their most popular engines as 'Hikers'. What Class of locomotive were they referring to?

3. Why was Kinnaber Junction so important during the 1895 'Races' between London and Aberdeen?

4. What was the number of 'The Diver'; the engine which went down with the Tay Bridge in 1879?

5. How many main line locomotive sheds were there in Fife in 1935?

6. How many classes of LNER 4-4-0 engines were there operating in Scotland in 1950?

7. How many platforms did Edinburgh's 'Waverley' station have in 1950?

8. One of the most numerous class of NBR freight engines was the LNER/BR J36. What made No. 65330 different from all the others?

9. What class of locomotive had the nickname of a NBR/LNER 'Jingling Geordie'?

10. Wick and Thurso are known as the two extremities of the Scottish network. At what junction do these two lines diverge?

11. What is the highest railway station is Scotland?

12. What 4-6-0 locomotive from the Highland Railway is preserved in the Glasgow Transport Museum?

Class 5 No 73114 *Elaine*, but what was the wheel arrangement of this loco?
Ken Wightman

Section 6
BR Standard Steam

1. How many Standard engines were built?

2. One engine only was fitted with a Giesl oblong ejector, which one?

3. What was the highest number allocated to a standard loco?

4. What engine was involved in the Milton accident in 1955?

5. Why was the coal space in the tenders of some class 4s working on the Southern Region split and in consequence giving reduced capacity?

6. What was unusual about 'Britannia' No 70047?

7. Only ten members of the 'Clan' class were built, but how many more were planned?

8. How many Class 5s were fitted with Caprotti valve gear?

9. What other type of Standard engine was also fitted with Caprotti gear?

10. What class of Standard tank had been considered to replace the LSWR 'O2' type on the Isle of Wight?

11. What class of Standard locos were built at Brighton?

12. What was unusual about the wheels on centre drive axle of a Standard Class 9?

13. The 9F design had also been proposed, with what wheel arrangement?

14. Some 9Fs were fitted with a Crosti pre-heater. From which country did this innovation come from?

15. Although a success working trains on the S&D, why were the 9F type not popular on this route in winter?

16. How many Class 5s working on the Southern Region were named?

17. Which classes of Standard engine were named under BR and how many in total carried names?

18. How many Britannia class locos are preserved?

19. The BR standard types were not universally liked on the WR except that is at one depot – which one?

20. Which was the last Britannia class engine in service?

21. There were two BR Class 4 tender engines, the 75xxx and 76xxx series. What was the principal difference between the two?

22. How many different classes of standard tank engine were built?

23. How many class 5 Standard locos are preserved?

24. Which side of the footplate were the Standard engines driven from?

25. How many Standard class types were tested on the Rugby test plant?

No. 92220 *Evening Star*, the last steam engine built for British Railways, but where was it built? *R. C. Riley*

No. 70014 *Iron Duke* whilst working on the Southern Region. So which London depot was responsible for providing the motive power for the 'Golden Arrow' train? *R. C. Riley*

Top: Former Class 33 now No 83 301. Why was it renumbered and what is unusual about this unique machine?

Bottom: What class of diesel is this?
Graham Smith courtesy Richard Sissons

Modern Traction 1

1. What was unusual about the Metrovick locos?

2. Before British Railways standardised on the 'Brush type 4' (Class 47) two other Type 4 diesels were on trial, what were they?

3. Who built the class 33 locos?

4. What was the horse power of a Class 20?

5. What type of transmission was used on the WR gas turbine loco No. 18000?

6. How many 'Deltic' class locos were built?

7. A spare body shell from a 'Deltic' was used in DP2. What did the initials 'DP' stand for?

8. In which country were a number of class 56 locos built?

9. What happened to brand new No. 70012 on 5 January 2011 as it was being unloaded at Newport Docks?

10. On what region of BR did the Brush type 2 (Class 31) originally work?

11. What was the origin of electric loco E2001?

12. What was unusual about the three SR electric locos Nos. 20001-3?

13. What were the 'LMS twins'?

14. Who designed the 4-8-4 later 4-4-4-4 diesel mechanical loco that operated on BR in the 1950s?

15. What was unusual about the design of wheels on the SR shunting engines introduced on to the SR in 1949?

16. What is a 'DEMU'?

17. 'APT-E' was a test design that operated on the LMR in the 1970s. What type of propulsion did it have?

18. What was unusual about 'APT-E' on curves?

19. Why did 'first generation' main live diesel locos often have to take on water at regular intervals?

20. What is the difference between a straight air brake and a train brake?

21. What is a drivers vigilance control?

22. On what LMR route did the Blue Pullman sets operate a regular service?

23. What was the nickname of the D95xx locos built at Swindon?

24. What were the origins of the class 74 electro-diesel type?

25. What was a 'master and slave' unit?

Nicknamed 'The chocolate zephyr', what was its proper identification and what is it?

Graham Smith courtesy Richard Sissons

No. 1504 but not in the UK.

What is it and in which country was it photographed?

Graham Smith courtesy Richard Sissons

GWR/WR stop and distant signals, plus a 'calling-on' at Stroud. The stop and distant arms are 'off' (at clear), at night a red light would show for 'danger' and a green light for 'clear'; so what colour were the glass lenses in the respective signals? *Graham Smith courtesy Richard Sissons*

Section 8

Signalling and Trackwork

1. What is the difference between ATC and AWS?

2. What is a trap/catch point?

3. In a mechanical signal box what colour is the detonator lever?

4. What does a flashing double yellow or single yellow signal mean to the driver?

5. What is an Annett's key?

6. What is an occupation key?

7. Why are there 'feathers' on some colour light signals?

8. What does the term 'ding-ding and away we go' mean?

9. What are track circuit clips?

10. What do the terms 'tappet', 'double twist', and 'stud' refer to?

11. What was 'Rule 55'?

12. What does the term 'fringe' signal box mean?

13. What is the Train Register?

14. What is an 'entrance-exit' panel?

15. What is a 'signal collar'?

16. What is tamping?

17. What is cant?

18. What is cab-signalling?

19. What might a periscope be used for in railway signalling?

20. Can you complete the following rhyme from years ago and relative to signalling; 'white is right and red is wrong, green means... (what)?'

21. What do the initials 'TRTS' mean on a plunger/button located on a station platform?

22. What is a bi-directional line?

23. What are the indications given by a three-position mechanical signal?

24. What does the term 'swallow tail distant' mean?

25. What is a 'switch diamond'?

Mechanical signal box and 'wheel'. What was the purpose of the wheel?
Transport Treasury

Why might signal posts be of differing heights? *R. C. Riley*

Train passing under a signal gantry, but what other term is often used to refer to a gantry carrying signals? *R. C. Riley*

Here we have two cranes working together on the recovery of a recalcitrant steam engine. When the actual lift commences a man will be stationed by the rear of each crane whose sole task is to observe the rearmost outer wheel of his crane – why?

Section 9

Accidents

1. What happened to Sir William Huskisson at the Rainhill trails of 1829?

2. Where is Quintinshill?

3. What were the circumstances of the Abermule disaster in 1921?

4. Was caused the permanent closure of the railway over the Severn Bridge?

5. What would happen if the water level in the firebox of a steam engine dropped so that the crown was exposed?

6. DP2 ended its days as a result of what accident?

7. In the event of an accident/derailment what are the first steps that should be taken by the train crew?

8. What happened at Grantham in 1906?

9. Bill Hoole was involved in an accident in 1948, where did it occur?

10. What was the cause of the Salisbury accident in 1906?

11. What happened at Norton Fitzwarren in 1941?

12. What caused the disastrous carriage fire near Penmanshiel tunnel in 1949?

13. Which locomotive was involved in the Ealing Broadway accident in December 1973?

14. In mechanical signalling what is the emergency bell code for 'obstruction danger'?

15. What were the purpose of 'safety chains' between vehicles?

16. What is a continuous brake?

17. What is a clearing point?

18. What is a 'Box to Box' special?

19. What does the term 'foot-notes' mean in a mechanical signal box?

20. What is the purpose of a lever collar?

21. What happened at Harrow and Wealdstone in November 1952?

22. What was steam engine invoked in the Lewisham disaster of 1957?

23. What occurred at Shrivenham in 1936?

24. What Is one engine in steam working?

25. If a train carrying passengers is required to pass over a facing point which is not or cannot be locked, what procedure must be followed?

Opposite top: This is the aftermath of the Salisbury derailment of 1906. The train involved was an Up LSWR passenger train, where from and who were they competing with in what was in effect a race?

Bottom: The collapsed flyover at Lewisham. What had caused it to collapse?

Nowadays also, an accident involving loss of life on the railway is investigated by the Department of Transport; in years past what other organisation as involved?

British Rail's 'APT' – this is the gas-turbine version – leaning to the curve on the Old Dalby test track.

Part A – Who wrote the original 'APT' book for Ian Allan?

Part B – What malady was found afflicted drivers of these very high speed train on curves?

Section 10
Railway Reading

1. Who wrote the history trilogy on the Great Central Railway?

2. O. S. Nock was a prolific railway author of a few years past, what was his profession?

3. Who was E. S. Cox?

4. What was the authors name of the series of hardback books on LNER locomotives?

5. Who was Colin Judge?

6. Jim Russell achieved fame with the early OPC, what for?

7. What was the profession of author and railway photographer R. C. Rlley?

8. What was the name of the official biographer of the GWR?

9. Which painter, who produced a number of paintings used in books and also advertising posters for British Railways always included his signature drawing of a mouse?

10. In what year did Ian Allan produce his first book of locomotive numbers?

11. What is the title of the regular periodical produced for members of the RCTS?

12. Which publisher produces books in the series 'Branch line to…' and 'Cross Country Railway Routes'?

13. Who has compiled most of the private owner wagon books for Black Dwarf/Lightmoor Press?

14. What book written by the late Bill Hudson describes in detail a railway route in the Peak district of Derbyshire?

15. What author's name is associated with a modern regular railway atlas currently in its seventh edition?

16. Name the author/compiler of the Modern Locomotives Illustrated magazine series?

17. A former GP from East Anglia produced several books on railways in his area who was he?

18. Who was R. H. N. Hardy?

19. Can you name two books by Peter Smith reminiscing on the Somerset & Dorset line?

20. Who was known as the honorary 'official' photographer of the Somerset & Dorset?

21. What were Messrs. Essery and Jenkinson renowned for?

22. Who is the author of the seminal series of books on Pullman cars?

23. Who had written extensively on the subject of Bulleid's 'Leader' class locomotive?

24. Up until recent times Messrs Ian Allan had four railway book and model shops in the UK where were they?

25. What was the name of the former politician who armed with a Bradshaw's guide travelled both the UK, Europe and America in a series of television programmes?

Opposite: Here we see a Bulleid coach but in unusual maroon with a 'W' prefix. Which author produced a scholarly work on 'Southern Coaches' and more recently a pictorial album 'Atmospheric Southern' for Transport Treasury?

Top: Preserved Drummond T9 No. 120 as running in BR days.
What author was responsible for the RCTS books covering the Beattie/ Adams/Drummond and Urie locomotives?

Bottom: Which publisher produces books on industrial locomotives based on defined areas? *All Graham Smith courtesy Richard Sissons*

'Jubilee' class 4-6-0 No 45572 *Eire*. Who is credited as having designed this class of engine?

Personalities

1. Who was Edward Thompson?

2. Who was the father of H. A. Ivatt of the LMS (not Mr. Ivatt Snr!) but another equally well known engineer?

3. Which company do you associate Richard Moon with?

4. Who was Sir Cyril Hurcomb?

5. What post did Major Maradin hold?

6. Why did the nameplate of No. 60525 *A. H. Peppercorn* only carry his initials and not his full name?

7. On which railway did O. V. S. Bulleid work immediately before going to the Southern?

8. With what railway do you associate the name James Inglis?

9. With with railway do you associate Ernest Lemon?

10. What post on the GWR did Daniel Gooch hold after that of locomotive engineer?

11. Who was Sir James Milne?

12. Who was Alfred Raworth?

13. Who designed a 2-6-0 locomotive with sleeve valves for the Midland Railway?

14. Who was Minister of Transport at the time of the Beeching Report?

15. Who was Richard (later Lord) Marsh?

16. Who is described as '…the best chairman BR never had'?

17. On which railway did George Jackson Churchward start his railway career?

18. In what year did Sir Nigel Gresley die in service?

19. With what would you associate the name Spagnoletti?

20. What was the first name of Mr. Fowler locomotive engineer to the Midland Railway and later the LMS?

21. Who designed the first Tay Bridge that collapsed in a storm at the end of 1879?

22. Gilbert Szlumper was General Manager of which railway?

23. Charles Bowen-Cooke was a locomotive engineer on which railway?

24. William Worsdell is associated with which company?

25. Where had Richard Beeching come from before his appointment as Chairman of BR?

The late lamented 'Brighton Belle'. Who was the General Manager of the Southern Railway at the time of its introduction in 1933?

Top: No mistaking No. 6000 *King George V* at Swindon running shed. Designed by Charles Collett and introduced in 1927; who succeeded Collett as CME of the GWR?

Bottom: Who designed this era of Waterloo & City underground stock?

Top and bottom: What are respective classes of these locomotives?

Section 12
Modern Traction 2

1. The Type 2 and Type 3 diesel locomotives produced by BRCW were of the same overall length. Precisely why was it possible for more power to be produced from the latter?

2. Which was the last 'Deltic' to receive a name and in what year?

3. Where might you expect to see the wording 'BR TIMKEN'?

4. To which communist country were supplied ten locomotives based upon the Brush Type 4 design in 1965?

5. Five manufacturers were appointed to construct prototype locomotives for the electrification of the West Coast Main Line in the late 1950s; name them.

6. Which Brush-built locomotive was at various times a Type 2 and a Type 4?

7. What was most significant about English Electric Type 1 D8128?

8. What was 'SSC' on a locomotive and what was its purpose?

9. The second 'Manchester Pullman' ran between which principal stations?

10. What was locomotive 'DP1' better known as?

11. Which locomotive builder had its main works at Queen's Park?

12. What is the difference between 'wheel slip' and 'wheel slide'?

13. Name the locomotive designer responsible for the original design of the 'Woodhead' route electric locomotives.

14. Which locomotives were given the class designation 'JA'?

15. Which Southern Region depot received an allocation of Sulzer Type 2s early on in their service life and why?

16. Which self-contained line became the first to be dieselised under BR?

17. What brought about the withdrawal of the 'Fell' diesel-mechanical locomotive in 1958?

18. Not all the power output of a diesel engine reaches the wheels for traction – give two reasons why this might be the case.

19. What does a higher route availability number normally represent?

20. Most locomotives renumbered under 'TOPS' carried similar numbers to what they originally carried e.g. D6713 became 37013. Why didn't D6700 become 37000?

21. What do the initials E.T.H.E.L. stand for?

This is a prototype unit that operated on the Southern and Scottish regions in the 1970s and early 1980s. What was their 'type' designation?

Graham Long courtesy Richard Sissons

Top: What was the wheel arrangement of this 'Peak' class locomotive?

Bottom: What is this the front end of?

Both Graham Long courtesy Richard Sissons

'Castle' class engine passing through Chipping Sodbury with the 'Pembroke Coast Express'. Chipping Sodbury is on what is referred to as the 'Badminton' line, but where does the 'Badminton' line run to and from?

George Heiron

Section 13
Railway Geography

1. What was the furthest station (distance wise) from Waterloo on the former Southern Railway?

2. What was the former name of the present Lincoln station?

3. Between 1948 and 1960 the two stations at Winchester were identified with suffixes, what were they?

4. The closed line to Brechin and Edzell had its junction at what station?

5. The railway geography at both Savernake and Marlborough was such that each had a 'High Level' and a 'Low Level' station. Which ones did MSWJ trains formerly use?

6. What do the initials PDSWJR stand for?

7. Where is Weaver Junction?

8. What was the name of the Somerset & Dorset station at Bath?

9. What line was popularised in the film 'Oh Mr. Porter!'?

10. Where does the Vale of Rheidol Railway (principally) start from?

11. Where is Bason Bridge?

12. What was the junction station for the former Mildenhall branch?

13. On what line was Woodford Halse station?

14. From Barry, a coastal route used to run to what other Welsh town?

15. There were once two stations at Ventnor, one was 'Town' what was the other?

16. Just south of Peebles a cross country route used to run west – to where?

17. Heading north, what is the next station after Biggleswade?

18. A branch once ran from Ledbury south to where?

19. Which of the stations at Barnstaple once made the connection with the narrow gauge Lynton & Barnstaple railway?

20. What station is on the opposite side of the estuary to Neyland?

21. What Cambrian Railway junction station was renowned for not having any road access (and as established primarily as an interchange point)?

22. There were once two branch lines off the main line on to Anglesey, can you name the termini of either?

23. What is the now closed station immediately south of Sheffield Park on the Bluebell Railway?

24. Which city in Devon might see a passenger depart for London by train in opposite directions?

25. Kemble was once the junction for two short branch lines, where to?

Above: A grimy 'V2' arrived at a London termini; which one?

Graham Smith courtesy Richard Sissons

Opposite Top: A USA tank at Eastleigh East. Straight ahead the line goes to Southampton but there is also a junction on the left – where to?

Opposite Bottom: Goring and Streatley is between which two principal stations (not the minor stations either side)?

Both Henry Priestley

What is the livery being carried by this Class 47?

Arthur Turner

UK railways since Privatisation

1. What were the origins of the Class 57 locos?

2. Where does Harry Needle have depot facilities?

3. Where are Arlington Fleet Services based.

4. What was the name for the shortened former HST sets operating on GWR?

5. What is the number of Class 66 *Evening Star*?

6. Class 73 locos originally operated mainly on what region of British Railways?

7. What is the difference between locomotives in classes 37/0 and 37/4?

8. What company are the three class 43 HST power cars normally used by Network Rail for its New Measurement Train hired from?

9. What are the northern and southern extremities of operation by Cross Country?

10. How many class 442 sets did South Western Railway take on with a view to refurbishing but then changed their mind?

11. What class 50 locomotive is operated by Hanson & Hall Rail Services?

12. No. 66783 has an unfortunate name associated with the type of train it might be found pulling. What is that name?

13. Which member of class 59 is in the GBRf pool?

14. How many vehicles does a class 800/0 have?

15. Who was the builder of the 'Desiro' class 707 units?

16. Which two Class 67 locos are painted in Pullman livery for VSOE work?

17. Where were Boden Rail Engineering based before their move to Nottingham?

18. Which class 47 was leased by Nemesis Rail to a Hungarian operator in 2015?

19. To which former Eastern bloc country were several Class 87 AC electric locomotives exported?

20. Where is the main engineering base for DB Cargo?

21. What was the original order for Javelin sets operating on HS1?

22. Where does the Parry People Mover operate?

23. Who has an assembly depot at Newton Aycliffe?

24. What is the length of HS1 between St Pancras and the Channel Tunnel?

25. What two London termini are used by the operator c2c?

What units are these and where might it have been taken?

Graham Smith courtesy Richard Sissons

Top: What is this unit?

Bottom: Two units of the same type at Loughborough. Can you identify the liveries?

Arthur Turner

This magnificent structure had once been the gateway to Euston – despite public outcry it was demolished when the station was rebuilt in the 1960s. What was it called?

Graham Smith courtesy Richard Sissons

Section 15
Pot Pourri

1. In what year was the Channel Tunnel opened?

2. What was the traditional colour of Pullman cars?

3. In which town/city was the Hunslet locomotive works based?

4. Where does the Talyllyn railway start from?

5. Which section of the Mid Hants railway was closed by BR in 1973 and did not subsequently open as a heritage line?

6. What is a track circuit?

7. What is an injector (on a steam locomotive)?

8. What is a buck-eye?

9. Tri-ang were for many years a prolific manufacturer of model railways, in which town was their UK headquarters?

10. What gauge was the Lee Moor tramway?

11. What is 'top dead centre' in relation to a steam engine?

12. What speed did *Mallard* reach on Stoke Bank on 3 July 1938?

13. What type of electrification was used by BR on the Manchester to Sheffield railway in 1955?

14. Approximately how many passengers used Waterloo station in 2022?

15. When was the original second class abolished by British Railways?

16. Where were the locomotive works of the Cambrian Railway company?

17. What do the initials M&GN stand for?

18. What is a tell tale (in relation to coaching stock)?

19. The GWR called them Camping Coaches, what did the LNER call them?

20. The Scot Dugald Drummond become locomotive superintendent of which English railway in 1895?

21. What is the jumping off station for rail passengers wishing to travel to the Isle of Skye?

22. Where and when was the last steam engine for British Railways built?

23. Who was James Holden?

24. What wheel arrangement was BR No. 60700?

25. What is the rail distance between Kings Cross and Edinburgh?

26. Where did the named train the 'Master Cutler' run to and from?

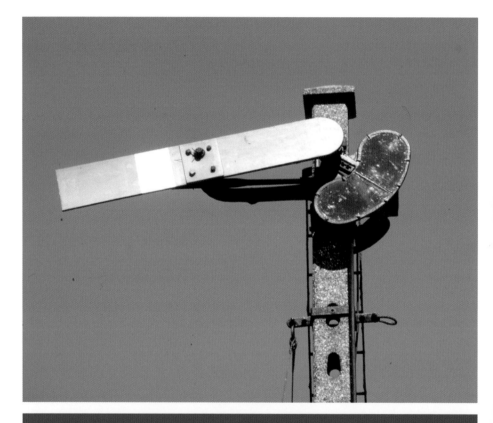

Above: What type of signal is this?

Opposite Top: How would a driver know which of these four ground disc signals applied to him?

Opposite Bottom: This type of steam engine was unusual – why?

All Graham Smith courtesy Richard Sissons

Answers

Page 5
Oval buffers were to be found on the front and rear of the BR Class 4MT 80xxx series and also on the front only of Class 8 No. 71000 *Duke of Gloucester*. They were considered necessary if the locomotive was considered particularly long and/or likely to be running on sharp curves and reduced the change of buffer lock. Oval buffers also appeared on the front of the 'Princess' and 'Duchess' class of the LMS.

Page 5 image
It is a 'MLV' – a Motor Luggage Van on the Southern Region.

Section 1 – GWR/WR – page 7

Page 6 The train is on the Up Relief line.

Page 7

1. 1835

2. No. 2935 *Caynham Court*.

3. V2 No. 60845 to trial a self cleaning smokebox.

4. Salisbury.

5. Part of the former Midland & South Western Junction line around Cirencester.

6. 1927 (although it may have taken a little time before all were repainted).

7. The lever was painted green.

8. A 'slipping distant' was a short armed distant signal which when lowered indicated to the driver – and slip guard - that he could indeed slip the appropriate portion of the train when passing through the platform.
    If however the slipping distant was 'on' then the driver would know he must in fact stop for the slip portion to be uncoupled in the normal way.

Page 8

9. Hawkridge Junction, also known as the Hawkeridge curve to Heywood Road.

10. 4' 6".

11. Sausages – from the Harris factory.

12. Told it was sweeter; Fry's chocolate.

13. Winchester.

14. 'Snake' was the code for a Passenger brake van. The telegraphic code also contained a number of others words mostly now forgotten, 'Lough' – 'Shunting horse ill – send relief', and 'Earwig' – 'Following urgently required'.

15. Joseph Armstrong; Northern Division 1854-1864 and Swindon 1864-1877.

16. Ingra Tor Halt on the Princetown branch

17. This is Bull-head track when the chair had the wooden key on the inside of the rail rather than on the outside as is more usual.

Page 9 The three answers are:

A. *Barningham Hall.*

B. Express freight without continuous brakes.

C. Warwick and Lapworth.

Page 10

18. Reading – and . Kays of Worcester and Paris.

19. Caersws.

20. Ranelagh Bridge; the previous depot was at Westbourne Park.

21. The Malmesbury branch.

Page 10 image

The class were originally numbered in the 48xx series, but in 1948 this number series was chosen to be used for engines of the 28xx type converted (as it turned out temporarily) to oil burning.

22. Frank Potter preceding and James Milne succeeding.

23. The answer is eight – five survive in preservation. The names were *King George, Queen Mary, Prince of Wales, Duke of York (s), Duke of Gloucester (s), Duchess of York, Princess Royal (s)* and *Princess Elizabeth.* Those marked with an (s) were scrapped.

24. Newburn House. Originally build for Joseph Armstrong in 1873 and later used by Mr Churchward, it was demolished in 1937.

25. The GWR used 26 inches compared with the other railway companies which used 21 inches. This meant that a non-GWR locomotive taking over a vacuum fitted train had to have the 'strings pulled' on all the vacuum fitted vehicles prior to departure to equalise the pressure in the brake cylinders and prevent the brakes from dragging.

Page 11 image

The shields are those from London and Bristol.

Section 2 – SR and Constituents – page 13

Page 12 image

The names were:

At the sign of the WHITE HORSE

At the sign of the JOLLY TAR

At the sign of the DOLPHIN

At the sign of the BULL

At the sign of the SALUTATION

At the sign of the THREE PLOVERS

At the sign of the GREEN MAN

At the sign of the GEORGE & DRAGON

Some of the cars also worked on the Eastern Region.

Page 13

1. 6,600V AC

2. Harry Holcroft – who also wrote two books of his experiences, 'Locomotive Adventure' published by Ian Allan.

3. The Dyke.

4. The answer is 50, 10 of the Merchant Navy class Nos. 35021-35030 and 40 Light Pacifics, Nos. 34071 to 34110.

5. The EiR tank class (from an E1 tank), the U class (from the former 'River' class tank engines, and the N15X class (from former L class 4-6-4T engines).

6. The original line was 3 feet gauge.

Page 14

7. Ashford, Lancing and Eastleigh.

8. Lock and Block. Put in its simplest form, once a train had been accepted the instrument was locked until the train depressed treadle indicating it had passed through the section.

9. HAL was half lavatory, meaning in a two car set only one half had a lavatory compartment.

10. Ventnor Town station, and the branch diverged at Merstone Junction.

11. Eustace Missenden commenced his railway career with the South Eastern & Chatham Railway company.

12. Simply put – it sunk. Folklore has it that whilst at Eastleigh it was deliberately filled with water to check it was water tight – which it was. There was then the problem of how to remove the water hence a hole was drilled in the keel. It appears the foreman in charge admitted his mistake with words similar to, 'I knew there was something we had to do (plug the hole) but I could not for the life of me remember what it was'.

13. Chapman Frederick Dendy Marshall, whose 'History of the Southern Railway' was first published in 1936.

14. Brighton.

15. The original name was Exeter Queen Street and the name changed in 1933.

16. Shalford Junction for the Redhill Line, and Peasmarsh Junction for the branch.

17. The answer is the Castleman's Corkscrew; Charles Castleman was a solicitor, justice of the peace, prison inspector and later chairman of the LSWR but who also promoted the Southampton and Dorchester railway.

18. The East Southsea branch from Fratton in Hampshire, and the branch from Weymouth (Melcombe Regis) to Easton in Dorset.

Page 15 image Yarmouth, Isle of Wight and Shirley Holmes Halt.

Page 16

19. This was on 10 July 1967 – delayed from 10 June and before that 1 January, both due to non-availability of the new rolling stock for the electric services. Folklore has it the date had been proposed to be put back even further but the condition of the remaining steam stock was by now so poor that there was every chance a service would not have been possible to be maintained.

20. The spare paths were known as 'Q' paths.

21. They are Messrs. Alan Blackburn, Gerry Bixley, Mike King and Ray Chorley.

Page 16 image The previous station would have been Ropley.

Page 17 image the locomotive is an 0415 class by William Adams.

Page 17

22. Mr. Bulleid came from the LNER where he had been Assistant to Gresley, and he left to go to Ireland.

23. Water pick-up apparatus – simply because the Southern had no water-troughs.

24. The trains went to Brookwood cemetery.

25. These were two 'Terriers' and given the numbers 734 and 735 by the LSWR. Neither was particularly successful on the branch and they were replaced by O2 and later 0415 type engines. No. 734 was later sold to the Freshwater, Yarmouth and Newport Railway in 1914 but returned to the Southern when that concern was absorbed in the Southern Railway in 1923.

Page 18 image The engines were nicknamed 'Black Fives'.

Page 19

1. The GWR at Swindon where he had previously been Works Manager.

2. Weaver Junction.

3. No. 6229 *Duchess of Hamilton*.

4. 1B was Camden, 1A was Willesden.

5. Wolverton.

6. Two, Blackpool Central (now closed) and Blackpool North.

7. The original Euston was designed by Philip Hardwick and built by William Cubitt. The present day station was designed by LMR architects William Robert Headley and Ray Moorcroft.

8. Josiah Charles Stamp was, amongst other post, Chairman of the LMS from 1926 until he and his family were killed in an air raid in 1941.

9. The experimental locomotive *Fury* blew a high pressure tube approaching Carstairs, killing a member of the test crew who was on the footplate.

10. Robert Riddles – usually referred to as 'Robin' Riddles.

11. The stated mileage of the LMS in route miles was 5,758 making it the largest of the four pre-nationalisation railways.

12. There were 35 in the class.

13. The principal constituents were:
    The Caledonian Railway, The Furness Railway, The Glasgow & South Western Railway, The Highland Railway, The London & North Western Railway (including the Lancashire and Yorkshire Railway), The Midland Railway. The North Staffordshire Railway.

14. The location was Rugby.

15. A 'Stove R' was a six-wheel brake van often used on parcels trains.

16. This was the almost brand new No. 46202 *Princess Anne*.

17. 'Litchfield' (with a 't') was on the GWR south of Newbury.

18. Just one, No. 44767.

19. This was the Stanier design 2-6-4T class.

20. The branch to Moffat.

21. A 'Baby Scot' was a class of locomotive having the chassis of a 'Royal Scot' together with the boiler from a 'Claughton', later also known as 'Patriot'.

22. There were three, Holyhead, Heysham, and Stranraer.

23. The height of the railway at Shap Summit is 916ft, 279m above sea level.

24. The viaduct at Ribblehead has 24 arches.

25. This was in 1913 when a passenger train collided with the rear of a another stationary passenger train. Several persons lost their lives.

Page 20 image The nickname was Big Bertha.

Page 21 image top *King George VI*, No. 46244 was a member of the 'Princess Coronation' class.

Page 21 image bottom Seen is the grandiose arched entrance to the engine shed at Inverness.

Page 22 image No. 60103 is of course *Flying Scotsman*.

Page 23

1. Kings Cross and Edinburgh.

2. This engine was known as Hush-Hush.

3. Charlie.

4. Liverpool Street.

5. Top Shed. (Bottom shed was the smaller one at Kings Cross itself.)

6. Stratford.

7. Doncaster.

8. The Great Central.

9. York.

10. A 'quad-art' set was a set of four coaches carried on five instead of the usual eight bogies – the coaches sharing single bogie except at the extreme ends of the set.

11. This was a Gresley design 2-8-2 locomotive intended to be used on heavy loads north of Edinburgh.

12. The Forth Bridge opened on 4 March 1890.

13. Takeley was on the line between Bishops Stortford and Braintree, opened in 1869 and closed to regular passenger services in 1952.

14. Varnished teak.

15. 'J' was an 0-6-0 (it mattered not if it were a tank or tender engine).

16. A total of 35 were built but only 34 entered BR service, No. 4469 originally *Gadwell* but renamed *Sir Ralph Wedgwood* from March 1939) destroyed in an air raid at York in 1942.

17. The answer is six, *Union of South Africa (Osprey), Woodcock, Dwight D. Eisenhower, Sir Nigel Gresley, Bittern*, and of course *Mallard*.

18. It was known as the Decapod, and having proved it could indeed accelerate a 320 ton train form a standstill to 30mph in 30 seconds, was later rebuilt into an 0-8-0 goods tender engine.

19. Sir Nigel Gresley 1923–1941, Edward Thompson 1941–1946, and Arthur Peppercorn, 1946–1947.

20. Driver James Gilbert and fireman James Nightall (posthumously) were recipients of the George Cross.

21. Bulleid 'light' Pacifics.

22. The 'Silver Jubilee' was a streamlined named train introduced in 1935 and operating between Kings Cross and Edinburgh.

Page 24 image The pipes were intended to take exhaust steam from the smokebox and by passing through colder water in the side tanks so convert this back into water. This was especially useful when working though tunnels in the London area. Similar equipment was fitted to several classes of locomotive (belonging to different companies) but was not always entirely successful.

Page 25 image It is of course *Tornado*.

23. A booster was a secondary steam engine which could be brought into action by the driver to provide additional tractive effort when needed – but of course at the expense of an additional drain on the boiler.

24. This was the first of what would become the EM1, later Class 76 Bo-Bo type.

25. Miles Beevor who had assumed the role earlier in 1947.

Section 5 – Scottish Railways – page 27

Page 26 images

Top: Cardenden.

Bottom: The engine is named *Blue Peter* (also the winner of the 1931 Derby).

Page 27

1. Sir Henry Fowler.

2. These were the LMS 'Black Fives'.

3. It was the 'winning post' for the respective East and West Coast trains.

4. North British Railway No. 224.

5. Five: Thornton, Dunfermline, and sub sheds Burntisland, Ladybank and Anstruther.

6. Ten. D11/2, D29, D30, D31, D32, D33, D34, D40, D41 and D49.

7. There were 21 platforms.

8. For a short while she was lined out in LNER apple green livery.

9. A member of the 'Scott' or D30 class.

10. Georgemas Junction.

11. This is Corrour on the West Highland line at 1,340ft (410m).

12. This is 'Jones Goods' No. 103.

Page 28 image The wheel arrangement is that of a 4-6-0.

Page 29

1. A total of 999.

2. 9F No. 92250.

3. Again, No. 92250.

4. No. 70026 *Polar Star*.

5. It was for reasons of weight when travelling over certain secondary and branch line routes.

6. The only one of the class not to carry a name.

7. Another 15 were planned.

8. 30 of the class.

9. The solitary Class 8 *Duke of Gloucester*.

10. The Class 2, 84xxx series. One actually arrived at Eastleigh for modification but the work was not proceeded with.

11. A total of 135 of the Class 4MT 2-6-4T 80xxx series.

12. The centre wheels did not have flanges.

13. The design was originally envisaged as a 2-8-2 tender engine.

14. The Crosti pre-heating fitments were devised in Italy.

15. Unfortunately the type were not fitted for steam heating.

16. Twenty of the class were given names formally carried by SR 'King Arthur' class engines.

17. A total of 76. 54 out of the 55 members of the Britannia class, the solitary Class 8 pacific, 20 Class 5s on the Southern Region and one 9F.

18. Two, No. 70000 *Britannia*, and No. 70013 *Oliver Cromwell*.

Page 30

19. Cardiff Canton.

20. No. 70013 *Oliver Cromwell*.

21. The 75xxx were 4-6-0 type and the 76xxx 2-6-0 type.

22. Three; the 80xxx, 82xxx, and 84xxx series.

23. There are five engines remaining in preservation.

24. All were driven from the left.

25. Examples of three standard classes were tested at Rugby; 'Britannia', 9F and Class 5.

Page 30 image *Evening Star* was built at Swindon.

Page 31 image The London depot was Stewarts Lane.

Section 7 – Modern Traction 1 – page 33

Page 32 images

Top: No. 83 301 is a former Class 33 fitted with replacement bogies for use on trials with Channel Tunnel trains prior to the commencement of regular services.

Bottom: This is one of the famed Class 59 diesels, imported from the USA and which revolutionised the reliability of stone haulage from the Foster Yeoman quarry in the Mendip hills.

Page 33

1. The Metrovick locos, D57xx were unusual in having a six-wheel bogie at one end and a four-wheel bogie at the other.

2. These were *Falcon* and *Lion*.

3. The Birmingham Railway Carriage and Wagon Company (BRCW).

4. 1,000hp.

5. An electric transmission, thereby making the engine accurately described as a 'gas-turbine-electric'.

6. You are correct if you say 22 or 23. There were 22 production locomotives for the Eastern Region but in addition there was the prototype.

7. 'DP' stands for 'Diesel Prototype'. *Deltic,* also built by English Electric was 'DP1'.

8. Romania.

9. No. 70012 was dropped from a crane at Newport Docks whilst being unloaded. Severe damage resulted and it was returned to the manufacturer.

10. The Eastern Region.

11. This had started life as Metropolitan Vickers Gas Turbine No. 18100.

12. All three had a 'booster' fitted, basically a massive flywheel that enabled the loco to negotiate short gaps in the third-rail system.

13. These were the two LMS main-line diesels, Nos. 10000 and 10001.

14. Lt. Col. L. F. R. Fell. It was known as the 'Fell' locomotive.

15. The 15 engines were fitted with 'BFB' (Bulleid-Firth-Brown) wheels as against conventional spoked wheels.

16. A Diesel-Electric-Mutiple-Unit.

17. Gas Turbines.

Page 34

18. It would tilt.

19. They were fitted with an oil fired steam boiler necessary to provide steam to heat carriages. (This was in the days before electric train heating.)

20. A straight air-brake operates on the locomotive only, the train brake operates on the locomotive and all the vehicles of the following train.

21. An automated device that requires the driver to lift his foot on and off a pedal – or other control – every set number of seconds to prove he is alert and awake. If he fails to respond within a set time the brakes are automatically applied.

22. The Midland main line from St. Pancras to Manchester via Derby.

23. Built at Swindon these were the 'Teddy-Bears'.

24. As a straight electric locomotive in the E50xx series

25. A permanently coupled pair of 350hp diesel shunting engines, only one of which had a driving cab.

Page 34 image This is 'GT3' more accurately 'Gas Turbine No. 3', a prototype from the 1960s which was not developed further.

Page 35 image A former 'EM2' 1500V DC electric locomotive, exported to the Dutch railway system when BR withdrew them from the Woodhead route where it had previously worked.

Section 8 – Signalling and Trackwork – page 37

Page 36 image The colours are red and blue and yellow and blue. Why blue and not green – the oil lamp behind used to illuminate the lens at night with a yellow flame; hence yellow passing through blue produces green.

Page 37

1. ATC was the original GWR safety equipment and only repeated the indication of the distant signals. AWS repeats not only the distant but all stop signals as well. In addition ATC was a contact based system, AWS is operated by induction magnets between the train and ramp with no physical contact made.

2. A point intended to deliberately derail a train/vehicle before it fouls another line.

3. Black with white chevrons. The chevrons pointing up for the up line and down for the down line.

4. A flashing signal means the train is to take a diverging route and the driver should reduce speed to that appropriate for the route.

5. A key which may sometimes be attached to or on the end of the single line token/staff which will unlock a ground frame/set of points.

6. Used by a ganger to guarantee occupation of a single line, but which key may be replaced in any one of a number of occupation key boxes and which will then free the line ready for the passage of a train.

7. To indicate a deviation from the main route. The 'feathers' consist of a line of white lamps. (Most now use five lamps.)

8. When the guard or other person instructs the driver to pull away with neither having confirmed the platform starting signal is clear. Several accidents have occurred as a result.

9. Emergency clips which may be clipped across the two running rails and which then show the signalman the track appears to be occupied. An occupied track means the signal for a train to approach cannot be cleared. Track circuit clips might then be used to protect an obstruction.

10. They all relate to types of mechanical lever frame interlocking.

11. Rule 55 stipulated that the driver/fireman (Second-man) on a locomotive stopped at a signal where the section of line was not track-circuited must attend the controlling signal box and sign the Train Register. Also to ensure the signalman places a reminder collar on the relevant signal to note his train is stationary.

12. The nearest adjacent mechanical box working to a power signal box.

13. The all important register in a mechanical signal box in which the times of all bell codes/passing trains are recorded.

14. A power signal box where the signalman sets a complete route by means of the pressing of a button at the point where the train enters his control and a second button at the point where he wishes the train to exit. The equipment checking the route, changing points as necessary and finally clearing the signals.

15. A reminder device placed on a signal lever to remind the signalman not to pull a particular lever. (Similar but smaller devices were available in MAS power boxes.)

16. Securing ballast tightly under and around sleepers, invariably achieved by powerful machines.

17. The relative angle of the track to the horizontal, one running rail against the other, usually on curves where one rail might be higher than the other.

18. When no trackside signals are provided and the speed the train may travel at coupled with the distance ahead the line is clear is shown to the driver.

19. This is to replicate the driver's sight line when considering the placing of a signal or as a result of a complaint re a signal's visibility.

Page 38

20. 'White is right and red is wrong, green means gently go along.'
It refers to the days when signal indication were red for stop, white for all clear, and green for caution.

21. Train Ready to Start - pressing the plunger would inform the signal box that station work was complete and the train is ready to depart.

22. A section of running line where a train might be signalled to run in either direction.

23. Vertical for all clear, 45 degrees up to the horizontal for caution and, horizontal for stop.

24. In the early days of the GWR the notch at the end of the distant signal arm was cut into a shape resembling a swallow tail – intended to prevent the wood from splitting.

25. A crossing where the rails may be mechanically aligned with the direction of travel. They are also known as moveable elbows.

Page 38 image
The signalman is operating a wheel to open or close level crossing gates.

Page 39 images

Top: The height of the post determines the importance of the route and speed.

Bottom: The official name for a signal gantry is a 'signal bridge'.

Section 9 – Accidents – page 41

Page 40 image The duty was to ensure the wheel did not lift from the track by even the smallest amount. Should this take place it could be a precursor to the crane tipping over – notwithstanding outriggers which may already be in position.

Page 41

1. William Huskisson was a VIP guest at the Rainhill Trials. He alighted his carriage and failed to move clear of an approaching train pulled by *Rocket*. Huskisson was struck and injured, injuries which later proved fatal.

2. Quintinshill is near Gretna Green on the Caledonian line between Glasgow and Carlisle. In terms of the number of casualties it was the worst railway accident in British railway history with over 200 fatalities.

3. The single line tablet was carried over into the next section and a train set off (therefore without authority) resulting in a head-on collision.

4. The structure was struck by a barge in fog in 1960. This brought down two spans. Repair was deemed uneconomic.

5. The fusible (lead) plugs would melt resulting in a rush of water and steam into the firebox often with catastrophic consequences to the crew on the footplate.

6. The engine was badly damaged when it collided with some derailed cement wagons near Thirsk in 1967.

7. To protect the scene.

8. A train failed to stop as scheduled at Grantham station instead continuing at speed until derailed on a sharp curve. The reasons were never fully explained.

9. New Southgate in 1948, engine No. 60508 *Duke of Rothesay*.

10. Excess speed through the station and on to a subsequent reverse curve.

11. Derailment, caused by the driver of a train on the relief line misreading the main line signals as his own.

12. A fire which set light to the new plastic type corridor side of a coach. The cause was thought to be a discarded cigarette – it had not been realised how flammable was the type of plastic covering.

13. Western class No (D)1007 *Western Talisman*.

14. Six bells.

15. An additional coupling used on early railways.

16. A brake that works on every vehicle of a train and may be applied on all vehicles at the same time.

17. A distance of 440 yards ahead of a signal showing 'danger' – in effect a safety over-run.

18. A special working details of which are passed by telephone from signal box to signal box.

Page 42 images

Top: The service had commenced from the docks at Plymouth Millbay. The GWR and LSWR were in competition to deliver mails and passengers as fast as possible to London via their respective routes. The GWR took the mails, the LSWR the passengers with the disastrous results seen.

Bottom: A supporting strut was hit by the steam train which had crashed into the rear of a stationary electric train at this point. This caused the bridge to collapse on to the derailed carriages below with tragic consequences. Fortunately another electric train just about to pass over the flyover managed to stop.

In previous years it was inspectors, invariably former Army Officers from the Royal Engineers who investigated and reported on accidents on behalf of the Board of Trade.

Page 43

19. 'Foot-notes' are local instructions applicable to the working of that particular signal box and authorised by the local signalling inspector.

20. To act as a reminder that the lever should not be pulled.

21. Three train collision in fog. Up express ran danger signal and collided with rear of stationary local train. Down express collided with the wreckage.

22. No. 34066 *Spitfire*.

23. A collision with stationary wagons. The guard of a goods train failed to recognise a coupling had broken and his van together with several wagons were marooned on the main line. They were then run into by a following express – the Guard having failed to protect his train in accordance with the rules.

24. A section of single line occupied by just one engine – or multiple engines coupled together.

25. The point must be 'clipped and padlocked'; meaning an elongated 'U' shaped clip is passed under the rail and the point blade which is then wound tight (clipped) and a padlock used to secure it in place.

Page 44 image

Part A: L. H. Williams for Ian Allan in 1985.

Part B: The tilt on curves was found to induce nausea to drivers.

Page 45

1. George Dow.

2. Mr. Nock was a railway signal engineer employed by Westinghouse at Chippenham.

3. E. S. Cox was one of the 'gang of three' (with Riddles and Bond) who were responsible for locomotive policy in the early days of the nationalised BR.

4. W. Yeadon.

5. Colin Judge was one of the founders of the original Oxford Publishing Company and also an author in his own right.

6. Jim Russell was a former Goods Guard but who produced several illustrated books for OPC in its early days on GW locomotives, carriages and wagons. He was also responsible for a book on the Banbury-Cheltenham line.

7. R. C. Riley was a banker.

8. This was E. T. MacDermot; he produced a three volume history of the company covering the years up to 1921.

9. Terrence Cuneo.

10. In 1942 when the young Ian Allan was employed by the Southern Railway. One of his tasks was to reply to members of the public enquiring about locomotives and so he suggested the SR might care to produce a book giving locomotive numbers. This was declined although he was permitted to do so himself – and at his own risk. He did with the results that are now well known – evidently Mr. Bulleid was not amused.

11. The RCTS produce the 'Railway Observer'.

12. Middleton Press.

13. Keith Turton.

14. 'Through Limestone Hills'.

15. Stuart Baker.

16. Colin Marsden.

Page 46

17. Dr. Ian C. Allen.

18. R. H. N. 'Dick' Hardy was a former Doncaster apprentice who went to senior positions on the Eastern Region and also served a period at Stewarts Lane. He wrote two autobiographies 'Steam in the Blood' and 'Railways in the Blood' as well as a book on Beeching.

19. 'Mendips Enginemen' and 'Footplate over the Mendips'.

20. Ivo Peters.

21. Bob Essery and David Jenkinson were respected authors of books on LMS subjects, in particular locomotives and rolling stock.

22. Antony Ford.

23. Kevin Robertson.

24. London (Waterloo), Birmingham, Manchester and Cardiff.

25. Michael Portillo.

Page 46 image Mike King.

Page 47 images

Top: D. L. Bradley.

Bottom: The Industrial Railway Society.

Section 11 – Personalities – page 49

Page 48 image (Sir) William Stanier.

Page 49

1. Edward Thompson was Chief Mechanical Engineer of the LNER from 1941 to 1946.

2. This was H. G. Ivatt, Locomotive Superintendent of the Great Northern Railway.

3. (Sir) Richard Moon was Chairman of the LNWR from 1861 to 1891.

4. Cyril Hurcomb (Sir) was the first Chairman of the British Transport Commission from 1948 until 1953. (Later Lord Hurcomb also the name given to 'Britannia' No 70001.)

5. Major Francis Maradin was an Inspector at the Board of Trade inspecting and testing railways in the latter part of the 19th century.

6. The nameplate would have been physically too long to fit in its designated place on the locomotive's smoke deflector!

7. O. V. S. Bulleid was assistant to Gresley on the LNER.

8. James Inglis was the former Chief Engineer and later General Manager of the GWR.

9. The LMS – as a former Chief Mechanical Engineer and later one of three Vice-Presidents.

10. General Manager from 1865 to 1899.

11. General Manager of the GWR after the departure of Sir Felix Pole until the end of the company in 1947.

12. The electrical engineer of the Southern Railway working at the same time as Bulleid.

13. Cecil Paget.

14. Ernest Marples.

15. Chairman of British Railways from 1971 to 1976. (A former Minister of Transport in the 1960s.)

16. Chris Green.

17. The South Devon Railway.

18. 1941.

19. Signalling equipment principally used on the GWR.

Page 50

20. Henry (Fowler).

21. Thomas Bouch.

22. The Southern Railway from 1937 to 1939.

23. The LNWR.

24. The LNWR, Pennsylvania Railroad, the GER and finally the NER.

25. Dr. Beeching was a physicist and engineer who came from ICI.

Page 50 image Sir Herbert Walker.

Page 51 images

Top: F. W. Hawksworth succeeded C. B. Collett.

Bottom: They were designed by O. V. S. Bulleid.

Section 12 – Modern Traction 2 – page 53

Page 52 images

Top: Electric E3021 Type 'A' later Class 81.

Bottom: D5405 and D5413 are former BRCW Type 2s, later designated Class 27.

Page 53

1. The Type 3 design didn't have a steam heating boiler and the resulting extra space permitted the installation of an eight cylinder engine instead of a six.

2. D9019 *Royal Highland Fusilier* in 1965.

3. On a locomotive axlebox cover.

4. Cuba.

5. English Electric, North British, Beyer Peacock, BRCW and BR Workshops.

6. D5835, which was temporarily uprated from 1365hp to 2000hp in 1963.

7. It was built four years after D8127, the first of a final batch of 100 units that were ordered following the declared failure of the Clayton type 1 design.

8. Slow Speed Control, for the haulage of loaded coal hoppers through power stations as their payloads were released automatically without stopping the train.

9. Manchester Piccadilly and London Euston.

10. DELTIC.

11. The North British Locomotive Company of Glasgow.

12. The former takes place when a loco loses traction under power, the latter is when its wheels lose grip under braking.

13. Sir Nigel Gresley.

14. The first six of the Southern Region's electro-diesels (later class 73/0).

15. Hither Green, to help eliminate steam traction in the Kent Coast electrification scheme because the intended BRCW Type 3s would not be delivered in time to achieve this.

16. The Wisbech & Upwell tramway in 1952.

Page 54

17. It was severely damaged by a fire at Manchester Central.

18. Transmission inefficiencies, generators are typically only 90% efficient, auxiliary equipment consumes power (e.g. ETH.).

19. A higher axle loading.

20. The 'TOPS' computer software didn't recognise any individual class member ending in three zeros; the next available free number tended to be used, in this case 37119 as No D6819 had already been withdrawn.

21. 'E.T.H.E.L.' stands for 'Electric train heating ex-locomotive. Three former Class 25 locos were converted to heat trains but were no longer able to self propel.

Page 54 image

They were designated 'PEP' units. ('Prototype-Electro-Pneumatic' train.)

Page 55 images

Top: The 'Peak' class (later class 44/45/46) were 1Co-Co1 designation.

Bottom: This is the front end of the prototype Class 252 HST.

Section 13 – Railway Geography – page 57

Page 56 image

The 'Badminton' line is also known as the 'South Wales Cut-Off' and runs from Wootton Bassett to Stoke Gifford (Bristol Parkway).

Page 57

1. Padstow at 259m 50ch.

2. It was previously Lincoln Central.

3. Winchester City (SR) and Winchester Chesil/Cheesehill) (WR later SR).

4. Bridge of Dun.

5. Savernake High Level and Marlborough Low Level.

6. Plymouth, Devonport and South Western Junction railway.

7. North of Crewe – it is the point where the lines to Liverpool and the north split.

8. Bath Green Park.

9. The Basingstoke and Alton Light Railway. (Cliddesden station being renamed 'Buggleskelly'.)

10. Aberystwyth.

11. On the S&D branch from Evercreech junction to Highbridge.

12. Fordham.

13. The Great Central Railway, the the LNER and Eastern Region route from Marylebone to Sheffield.

14. Bridgend.

15. The second was Ventnor West.

16. Symington.

17. Sandy.

18. Gloucester.

19. Barnstaple Town.

Page 58

20. Pembroke Dock.

21. Dovey Junction.

22. Amlwch, and Redwharf Bay & Benllech.

23. Newick & Chailey.

24. Exeter St. Davids.

25. Tetbury to the west and east to Cirencester Town.

Page 58 image Kings Cross.

Page 59 images

Top: The junction to the left is the line to Fareham and originally Gosport.

Bottom: The major stations either side are Reading and Didcot.

Section 14 –
UK railways since Privatisation – page 61

Page 60 image
This is the livery for 'RES' (Rail Express Systems).

Page 61

1. Rebuilt from Class 47.

2. Worksop and Barrow Hill.

3. Eastleigh.

4. 'Castle' sets.

5. No. 66779.

6. The Southern Region.

7. Class 37/4 locos are fitted with an electric train supply (for heating and air conditioning).

8. Porterbrook.

9. Aberdeen and Penzance.

10. 18.

11. No. 50008 *Thunderer*.

12. The Flying Dustman.

13. No. 59003 *Yeoman Highlander*.

14. Class 800/0 are five-car units.

15. Siemens.

16. Nos. 67021 and 67024.

Page 62

17. Washwood Heath, Birmingham.

18. No. 47375.

19. Bulgaria.

20. Toton, near Nottingham.

21. 29 six-car trains

22. Between Stourbridge Junction and Stourbridge Town.

23. Hitachi.

24. 67 miles.

25. Fenchurch Street and Liverpool Street.

Page 62 image These are class 442 units at Waterloo.

Page 63 images

Top: The unit is 'IRIS 2' formed of two DMU coaches previously a Class 101 Metropolitan-Cammell unit. It was converted in 1991 by the BR Research Department as a radio Surbey Unit and taken on by Serco Railtest Ltd.

Bottom: The two sets are, (left) in the livery of Central Trains, and (right) in Midland Mainline livery.

Section 15 – Pot Pourri – page 65

Page 64 image It was known as the Doric Arch.

Page 65

1. 1994.

2. Umber and cream.

3. Leeds.

4. Tywyn.

5. Alresford south through the station at Itchen Abbas to Winchester Junction.

6. An electric device which indicates the position of a train/vehicle on a particular section of track.

7. A means by which cold water can be injected into the boiler of a steam locomotive against the pressure within the boiler.

8. A coupling between items of rolling stock. This type of coupling also holds the vehicles tightly clamped together.

9. Margate.

10. 4' 6".

11. When the engine stops in such a position that steam entering the cylinders is unable to expand sufficiently on either side of the piston to effect movement.

12. 126 mph.

13. 1,500V DC.

14. 41,326,000.

15. In June 1956 the original second class was abolished and third class redefined as second class.

16. Oswestry.

17. Midland & Great Northern Railway.

18. This is a device which moved from one position to another, should the communication cord be pulled by a passenger within that coach. The guard might thus be able to identify in which vehicle the cord had been pulled.

19. Caravan coaches.

20. The London & South Western Railway.

Page 66

21. Kyle of Lochalsh.

22. Swindon in March 1960; No. 92220 *Evening Star*.

23. James Holden had been chief assistant to William Dean on the GWR at Swindon but left to become Locomotive Superintendent of the Great Eastern Railway in 1885.

24. It had the wheel arrangement 4-6-4.

25. 393 miles.

26. Between London Marylebone and Sheffield.

Page 66 image

This is a somersault signal – notice the centre pivot.

Page 67 images

Top: One of the four discs will rotate through approx one-eighth of a turn. The rule is 'top to bottom = left to right', therefore the top most disc refers to the line furthermost to the left and so on.

Bottom: It is a fireless locomotive. The boiler would be filled with pressurised steam at the start of operations and the engine could then work safely without emitting sparks or cinders.

If you are one of those people who start from the back,
No 71000 *Duke of Gloucester* is one of the answers to the question on
page 5.

So can you work out what the question might be?